This book belongs to

....

Quarto is the authority on a wide range of topics.

Quarto educates, entertains and enriches the lives of our readers—enthusiasts and lovers of hands-on living.

www.quartoknows.com

© 2019 Quarto Publishing plc

First published in 2019 by QED Publishing, an imprint of The Quarto Group.
The Old Brewery, 6 Blundell Street,
London N7 9BH, United Kingdom.
T (0)20 7700 6700 F (0)20 7700 8066
www.QuartoKnows.com

A catalogue record for this book is available from the British Library.

ISBN 978-1-78603-602-5

Based on the original story by Kate Tym and Jana Christy
Author of adapted text: Katie Woolley
Series Editor: Joyce Bentley
Series Designer: Sarah Peden

Manufactured in Dongguan, China TL112018

9 8 7 6 5 4 3 2 1

MIX
Paper from responsible sources
FSC® C104723

Reading
Gems

Fun at the Beach

Mum said, "Look,
the sun is here today."

Dad said, "Let's go to the sea to play!"

We jumped in the car.
It went off with a screech.

It was time for us all
to go to the beach!

At the beach, we ran hand in hand.

"Let's go and make sandcastles in the sand."

I can make a great big sandcastle!

Then everyone wanted
to jump in the sea.

What a splash I can make!
"Mum, look at me!"

Buckets and spades,
balls and bats.

"Put on sun cream. Put on hats!"

Dad got ice creams
for everyone.

Then Mum cleaned us all up in the sun.

Clean up!
Ice cream
everywhere!

After ice creams, we ran to the big funfair.

The rides went here, there and everywhere!

Go up, go down,
bend after bend.

Look at me,
Mum!

Dad soon wanted the rides to end.

The funfair had games
for us all to play.

But soon it was the end of the day.

We got in the car. "Goodbye, beach."

Off went the car with a great big screech.

Story Words

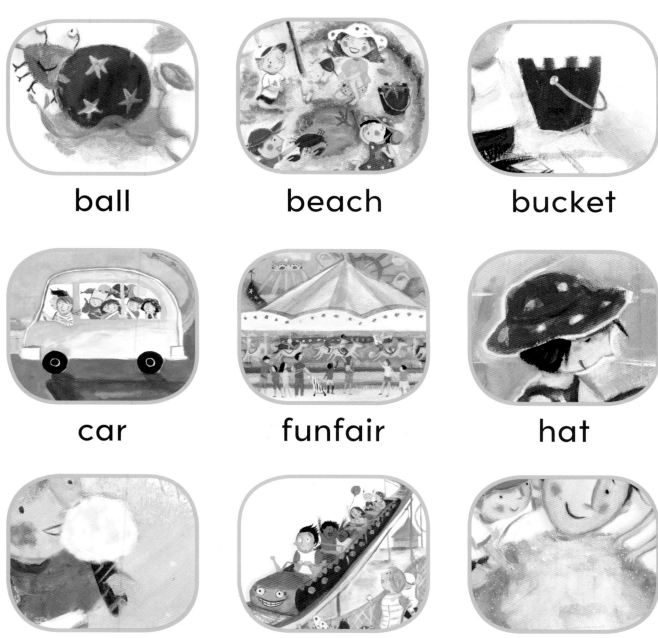

ball

beach

bucket

car

funfair

hat

ice cream

ride

sand

sea

spade

sun

sun cream

Let's Talk About Fun at the Beach

Look at the book cover.

Talk about the weather. Is it sunny or raining? How can you tell?

What do you like to do on sunny days and rainy days?

The car goes off with a 'screech'.

Can you make that sound?

What other sounds do cars make?

The family all go to a funfair.

What do they do at the fair?

Why does Dad want to get off the rides?

Have you ever been to a fair?

Do you like funfair rides?

The family play games on the beach, jump in the sea and go to the funfair.

What else can you do at the beach?

What do you like to do as a family?

Did you like the story?

What was your favourite bit?

Fun and Games

Unscramble the words. Then match
each word to the correct picture.

cubekt   hpsla   eas   nufrfia

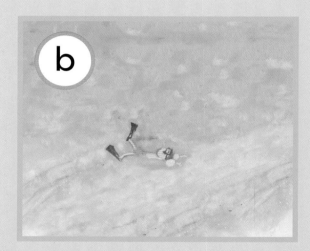

The car needs to get to the beach.
Which path should Dad take?
Find the initial letter sound for the
word 'beach' to find the right path.

b   k   g   s

Your Turn

Now that you have read the story,
have a go at telling it in your own words.
Use the pictures below to help you.

GET TO KNOW READING GEMS

Reading Gems is a series of books that has been written for children who are learning to read. The books have been created in consultation with a literacy specialist.

The books fit into five levels, with each level getting more challenging as a child's confidence and reading ability grows. The simple text and fun illustrations provide gradual, structured practice of reading. Most importantly, these books are good stories that are fun to read!

Phonics is for children who are learning their letters and sounds. Simple, engaging stories provide gentle phonics practice.

Level 1 is for children who are taking their first steps into reading. Story themes and subjects are familiar to young children, and there is lots of repetition to build reading confidence.

Level 2 is for children who have taken their first reading steps and are becoming readers. Story themes are still familiar but sentences are a bit longer, as children begin to tackle more challenging vocabulary.

Level 3 is for children who are developing as readers. Stories and subjects are varied, and more descriptive words are introduced.

Level 4 is for readers who are rapidly growing in reading confidence and independence. There is less repetition on the page, broader themes are explored and plot lines straddle multiple pages.

Fun at the Beach is a rhythm and rhyme story all about a family's seaside adventures. It explores themes of family life and the seaside environment.

Level 2

Short sentences ✓

Simple vocabulary ✓

Buckets and spades, balls and bats.

"Put on sun cream. Put on hats!"

Some repetition ✓

Pictures and words support one another ✓